A Gift for:

_____

From:

_____

Pets' Letters to God 2

© 2007 by Hallmark Licensing, Inc. and Rodale Press. This edition published
under license from Rodale Press by Hallmark Books, a division of
Hallmark Cards, Inc., Kansas City, MO 64141

Visit us on the Web at www.Hallmark.com.

Editorial Director: Todd Hafer
Art Director: Kevin Swanson
Designer: Sarah Smitka/The Pink Pear Design Co.
Cover Design: Mary Eakin
Production Artist: Dan Horton

ISBN: 978-1-59530-167-3

BOK2079

Printed and bound in China.

pets' letters to God 2

GIFT BOOKS
from Hallmark

Introduction

Ever wonder what our pets are thinking? You can bet they often wonder what we're thinking! But try though they might to ask us, our answers—if we even bother to respond—usually confuse them even more. Lucky for them that God has a lot more patience (not to mention language skills) than we do.

In this book, you'll find a selection of questions about what goes on in heaven, how pets get their names, why we people act so strange, why cats (or dogs) get special treatment, and many other pet-perplexing probings. We hope they make you laugh, cry, think and, of course, wonder what God's answers might be.

Why don't you share your favorite questions with your pets? You might see a knowing twitch of your cat's tail...or a grin on your dog's face.

HATE is a bad guide. I have never considered myself at all a good hater—though I recognize that from moment to moment hate has added stimulus to pugnacity. *House of Commons, November 6, 1950*

Mr. Churchill was dozing his way through a long, boring speech in the House of Commons. The speaker suddenly noticed him and asked loudly, "Must you fall asleep when I am speaking?" Mr. Churchill answered, "No, it's purely voluntary."

The Chain of Destiny:
Governments and Policies

At the age of 76, Winston Churchill was recalled to the office of Prime Minister. In return for his dedication to public service, he had won every accolade his country could offer. But he wanted to help build a permanent peace. "That is the last prize I seek to win," he said.

IN DEALING with nationalities, nothing is more fatal than a dodge. Wrongs will be forgiven, sufferings and losses will be forgiven or forgotten, battles will be remembered only as they recall the martial virtues of the combatants; but anything like chicanery, anything like a trick, will always rankle.

House of Commons, April 5, 1906

I SUPPOSE we are admirers of the party system of government; but I do not think that we should any of us carry our admiration of that system so far as to say that the nation is unfit to enjoy the privilege of managing its own affairs unless it can find someone to quarrel with and plenty of things to quarrel about. *House of Commons, December 17, 1906*

I WILL not pretend that, if I had to choose between

47

Communism and Nazism, I would choose Communism. I hope not to be called upon to survive in the world under the Government of either of those dispensations. *House of Commons, April 14, 1937*

I ENTIRELY agree that the civil authority has supreme authority over the military men.

IT IS a mistake to look too far ahead. Only one link in the chain of destiny can be handled at a time.

House of Commons, March 14, 1938

I CANNOT forecast to you the action of Russia. It is a riddle wrapped in a mystery inside an enigma: but perhaps there is a key . . . Russian national interest.

World Broadcast, October 1, 1939

EVERYBODY has always underrated the Russians. They keep their own secrets alike from foe and friends. *House of Commons, April 23, 1942*

AT THE bottom of all the tributes paid to democracy is the little man, walking into the little booth, with a little pencil, making a little cross on a little bit of paper—no amount of rhetoric or voluminous discussion can possibly diminish the overwhelming importance of that point.

House of Commons, October 31, 1944

THERE was a custom in ancient China that anyone who wished to criticize the Government had the right to memorialize the Emperor and provided he followed that up by committing suicide, very great respect was paid to his words, and no ulterior motive was assigned. That seems to me to have been from many points of view a wise custom, but I certainly would be the last to suggest that it should be made retrospective.   *House of Commons, November 12, 1941*

SOMBER indeed would be the fortunes of mankind if some awful schism arose between the Western Democracies and the Russian Soviet Union, if the future world organization were rent asunder, and if new cataclysms of inconceivable violence destroyed all that is left of the treasures and liberties of mankind.   *House of Commons, February 27, 1945*

IF YOU destroy a free market you create a black market.

ALL SOCIAL reform which is not founded upon a stable medium of internal exchange becomes a swindle and a fraud.   *Brighton, October 4, 1947*

MANY forms of government have been tried and will be tried in this world of sin and woe. No one pretends that Democracy is perfect or all-wise. Indeed,

49

it has been said that Democracy is the worst form of government except all those other forms that have been tried from time to time.

Democracy is not a caucus, obtaining a fixed term of office by promises, and then doing what it likes with the people . . . . Government of the people, by the people, for the people, still remains the sovereign definition of democracy.

House of Commons, November 11, 1947

THE WORLD moves on and we dwell in a constantly changing climate of opinion. But the broad principles and truths of wise and sane political action do not necessarily alter with the changing moods of a democratic electorate. Not everything changes. Two and two still make four and I could give you many other instances which go to prove that all wisdom is not new wisdom.   *Belle Vue, December 6, 1947*

I TELL you—it's no use arguing with a Communist. It's no good trying to convert a Communist, or persuade him. You can only deal with them on the following basis . . . you can only do it by having superior force on your side on the matter in question —and they must also be convinced that you will use —you will not hesitate to use—these forces if necessary, in the most ruthless manner.

You have not only to convince the Soviet Government that you have superior force—but that you are not restrained by any moral consideration if the case arose from using that force with complete material ruthlessness. And that is the greatest chance of peace, the surest road to peace.

New York, March 25, 1949

LAWS, just or unjust, may govern men's actions. Tyrannies may restrain or regulate their words. The machinery of propaganda may pack their minds with

51

falsehood . . . . But the soul of man thus held in trance or frozen in a long night can be awakened by a spark coming from God knows where . . . . Peoples in bondage need never despair.

Massachusetts, March 31, 1949

THE REASON for having diplomatic relations is not to confer a compliment but to secure a convenience.

House of Commons, November 17, 1949

APPEASEMENT in itself may be good or bad according to circumstances. Appeasement from strength is magnanimous and noble and might be the surest and perhaps the only road to world peace.

House of Commons, December 14, 1950

ONE OF the disadvantages of dictatorships is that the dictator is often dictated to by others, and what he did to others may often be done back again to him.

SOLVENCY is valueless without security, and security is impossible to achieve without solvency.

THE DAY will come when it will be recognized without doubt throughout the civilized world that the strangling of Bolshevism at birth would have been an untold blessing to the human race.

House of Commons, May 11, 1953

It is an error to believe that the world began when any particular party or statesman got into office. It has all been going on quite a long time.

If a Government has no moral scruples it often seems to gain great advantages and liberties of action, but, "all comes out even at the end of the day, and all will come out yet more even when all the days are ended."   from *The Second World War*

Set in Linotype Aldus, a roman with old-face characteristics, designed by Hermann Zapf. Aldus was named for the 16th century Venetian printer Aldus Manutius.
Typography by Grant Dahlstrom, set at The Castle Press.
Printed on Hallmark Eggshell Book paper.

Designed by Harald Peter.

Contents

8
When I Get to Heaven...

33
The Name Game

46
Reigning Cats and Dogs

79
Just Wondering...

When I Get to Heaven...

We're not the only ones who wonder what heaven is like. As you'll see from the letters in this chapter, our pets have a lot of questions about their future home—and like us, they're hoping it will be a comfy one!

Dear God,
    Are clouds really as
soft and comfy as they look?
And if so, do we each get our own?

        Here's hoping,
        Marcus

Dear God,

My person tells me that heaven is up in the sky, but I feel certain it's underground somewhere, since that's where all the good stuff is—like bones and old chew toys. I keep digging and digging, but I can't find heaven. I don't suppose you have a map anywhere?

Still digging,
Max

M

Dear God,
Can I have a halo
of butterflies in heaven?

Marlo

Dear God,
  Are cats bigger than dogs in heaven?
           Hopefully, Jessi

Dear God,
    Heaven looks a lot like a giant aquarium from down here. Does that mean when I go there I'll be a catfish?

(I can't swim.)

Love,
Sybil

Dear God,
  Are there bones in heaven?
Lots of bones? A bounty of bones?
Just checking.

                    Sam

PS. I like bones.

Hi, God,

I was wondering, since the grass is blue in heaven instead of green, could I be a different color, too? I think I'd like a green coat with peach stripes, blue paws, and a red tail. Don't worry if you can't remember this. I'll remind you when I get there.

Your friend,
Linus

Dear God,
    Scratching, licking, biting, rolling...aaahhh!
For some reason, my human family just hates
it when I'm doing anything that feels good.
I'm hoping you're more tolerant in heaven!

    —Thor

Dear God,
   Do you need an interpreter up there in heaven? I can speak dog, cat, and human, if that would be any help.

   Just let me know,
      Plutarch the Parrot

Dear God,
    Can I chase my tail in heaven
and not get yelled at? And is there any chance
that I'll finally catch it?

                    Just thought I'd ask,
                    Caesar

Dear God,
     How far must I fly
before I get to heaven?

—Willow

Dear God,

    When I go to heaven, can I lie on the couch whenever I want? With a bowl of buttered popcorn with cheese on it? How about some classic movies like *Old Yeller* and *Lassie, Come Home*?

    Also, I don't want to push my luck here, but is there any hope for a paw-friendly remote control?

                  Cinematically yours,
                  Sampson

Dear God,
    Do I have to have a pedigree
to get into heaven, or is being one
of your creatures pedigree enough?

                    Optimistically,
                         Dozer

NOAH

Dear God,
   I understand we snakes have a bad rep in some religious circles. So I'm wondering, Are there any snakes in heaven?
(I haven't done anything wrong, by the way.)

—Noah the Boa

Dear God,

Can I have a word with Ben Franklin when I get to heaven? If it weren't for him and his doggone kite, there would be no electric dog fences! Couldn't he just have invented automatic treat dispensers and left it at that?

No friend of Ben,
Jefferson

Dear God,
    Are there catnip mice in heaven? How about
real mice that taste like catnip? Please?

—Mittens

Dear God,
    Is there a place in heaven just for bunnies?
We're going to need a lot of room up there...

        Thanks for answering,
        Sasha

Dear God,

Is heaven like a huge terrarium, full of warm rocks, heat lamps, and crickets (but no plastic pirates and castles)? Sure sounds heavenly to me!

—Gilbert Gecko

Dear God,
    I've heard that when people arrive in heaven, they're met by St. Peter at the Pearly Gates. So I was wondering, is there a special gate for pets in heaven? And if so, will St. Francis be there to meet us?

        A St. Francis fan,
            Shawn

St. Francis

The Name Game

As **T.S.** Eliot pointed out, the naming of cats is a difficult matter. And the same goes for dogs, turtles, birds, bunnies, guinea pigs, and even fish. Like us, our pets have strong opinions on their names, as you'll soon see.

Dear God,
    When I was a kitten, my person named me Fluffy. As a 30-pound adult male, I resent this. How can I give her the hint?

Had enough,
Big Daddy (not Fluffy)

Dear God,

My person is a classics professor. This doesn't sound too bad, but he named me Alcibiades, and then he named the parrot Metellus! Now no one will talk to us. I think they're embarrassed. I know I am! Can you ask people to stick with one- or two-syllable names that are easy to say, please?

Your pal,

Al (for short)

Dear God,
   Are you and I, by any chance, related? Half the time my people seem to refer to me as "Good God!" and "Oh, my God!" They must think I'm deaf as well since they're usually shouting. You know, I always hoped you might be a dog!

                    Your cousin(?),
                    Sam

Dear God,
Can I pick my own name in Heaven?
Paws crossed, Precious

Dear God,
   Don't fish have names? Our human family is always watching us, but they never call us anything. This makes us very self-conscious.

   Please advise,
The fish of the Walker family tank

Dear God,

My family told the baby, then age three, that she could choose my name. She chose "Tunahead." When I go to Heaven, do I get to name her?

Waiting,
    Mr. T. Head

Dear God,

My name is Greyfax—a dignified, respectable name for a distinguished feline such as myself. Unfortunately, my person seems to have forgotten this. Instead, she addresses me by a revolting array of babyish babble, including "Sweetums" and "Twinkle," just to name a few. I always hold my head high so she can see the name "Greyfax" plain as day on my collar, but she never takes the hint. Would you remind her, please?

Gratefully,
Greyfax

Dearest God,
    Do you know all our names?

        Wondering,
        Marley

Dear God,
    The other dogs in my neighborhood
are named Rocky, Spike, Harley, Wolf,
and Grizz. What were my people thinking
when they decided to name me?

                —Frodo

Dear God,

Everyone laughs when he or she hears my name. Well, I may be small, but I am mighty! Let's see people try to walk around carrying their houses!

—Hercules the hermit crab

Dear God,
    Did you have to give humans such a warped sense of humor? Because I'm a fish, they insisted on naming me Huckleberry Finn. Get it?! If you decide to recall them, perhaps you could work on this.

    —The Mighty Finn

Dear God,
    My person named me Angel. Does this mean
I have wings? I keep rolling over, but I can't feel them.
Thanks for clearing this up.

                        Confused,
                        Angel

Reigning Cats and Dogs

Dogs and cats have a lot to say about themselves, each other and, of course, us. Take a peek in God's mailbag and see for yourself!

Dear God,

I'm sent to obedience school; the cat sleeps. I'm told to do this, fetch that; the cat eats. I'm punished for every little thing; the cat licks herself. Why am I expected to obey when the cat does whatever she wants? I hate to complain, but it really doesn't seem fair.

Wondering,
MacArthur

Dear God,
My people "go out to eat" all the time. But whenever I go out to eat, I get in trouble! Are they jealous because I found the dead rabbit first?

Puzzled,
Homer

Dear God,
   Just once, could I have the pizza
and not just the crust?

              Hopefully,
              Lucky

Greetings, God,

What's the difference between the carpet on the scratching post and the carpet on the floor?

Am I missing something here?

Confused,
Alice

Dear God, People are always telling me
I ain't nothin' but a hound dog. What
do they mean, anyway?!   —Elvis

Dear God,

I wanted to put in a good word for my person. She hugs me and tells me she loves me several times a day, and she plays with me and gives me treats. She also talks to me and asks for my advice, though as far as I can tell, she hasn't ever taken it. But I can see she's really trying! Just thought you ought to know.

Thanks for listening,
Jordan

Dear God,
Are tires the ultimate chew toy?

—Chito

Dear God,

Life was perfect when I was an only cat, but now my family has adopted two strays. I've tried to help them escape, but to no avail. I understand that murder is not an option. What's the alternative?

Missing the good old days,
Athena

Dear God,
  Why do people think "fetch" is good but "chase" is bad? They're both fun to me!

—Tom

Dear God,
    Can't you make another commandment about fur dyes, nail polish, perfumes, and bows for dogs? We're dogs, not dolls! A good "Thou shalt not" should do the trick.

        Thank you,
    Missy, Joelle, and Babs

Dear God,
What's the deal? Cats have nine lives, but we dogs just get one! Can you revisit this inequity, please?

Only one life to live,
Chevy

Dear God,
     Every day, the dog eats his food;
then he eats mine. You'd think someone
would notice, but noooooo! Then, when I
jump up on the table and try to take a
bite or two of steak or a couple of shrimp—
just to sustain life, you understand—who
gets the blame? What's a poor cat to do?

          Counting on you,
               Chrissie

Dear God,

How was I supposed to know the yarn wasn't a toy?!

In disgrace,
Xena

Dear God,
    If they didn't want me to eat it, why'd they leave it on the counter?!

Clueless,
    Caesar

Dear God,
 Why do I have to wear a collar
and leash, but the cat strolls around
unfettered? Is there no justice?!

—Rory

Dear God,
    Shedding. Coughing up hairballs. Clawing the woodwork. Unraveling a month's knitting. Running around the house all night. Yowling. A cat's work is never done!

—Maxine

Dear God,

Why is it that people get to eat different food at every meal, but I get the same food day in, day out? Dogs like variety, too!

Chowed out,
Brutus

Dear God,
    Thanks for giving me and my sister Layla the ultimate toy: our cat Molly. She is fun to bark at, lick, run up trees, steal food from, bat, sleep on, and many other good games. We especially love chasing her long, plumed tail. And best of all, she never wears out! You really do think of everything!

                Your friend,
                Linus

Dear God,
 More mud puddles, fewer baths, please!

 Thanks in advance,
 Chester

Dear God,
      If dogs weren't supposed to mark
trees, why are they covered in bark?

                    Logically,
                    Jeeves

Dear God,
    Well, I guess they didn't like the mouse. I was just trying to share!
            Bemused,
            Bramble

Dear God,
    I love cars. They are the greatest thing you ever invented, and that includes Frisbees and even fire hydrants. Thank you so much!!! But, um, if it wouldn't be too much to ask, do you think I could drive one?

            Crazy for cars,
            Comet

Dear God,
    Can't people take a hint?
Why do they think they're called
"doggie bags"?!

        Aggravated and hungry,
        Rufus

WALLACE

Help, God!

It wasn't my fault I got sprayed by a skunk. (Well, maybe it was.) But it's not like I was trying to get sprayed, for Pete's sake. So why is my family putting tomato juice all over me? Are they planning to eat me? Please tell them I'll never chase a skunk again if they go for the burgers instead!

Nervously yours,
Wallace

Dear God,
    I thought I had a good grasp of Human, but I just don't see how "'Tis the season to be jolly" translates to "Keep away from the Christmas tree!" "Don't bat the ornaments!" "That milk is for Santa!" "Stay away from the fireplace!" "Stop shredding those ribbons!" and on and on. Some holiday!

                                        Trying to be jolly,
                                        Sadie

Dear God,
    You made squirrels. You made bird feeders. You made soft grass. Did you have to make me an indoor cat?!

        Frustrated,
        Fiona

Dear God,
    Are aquariums really cat TVs?
If they are, how can I change the channel?

        Sick of the Guppy Channel,
            Margot

Dear God,

Please tell the cat to get off my bed. He's so small, yet he seems to take up all the space. Now I'm sleeping on the floor. Why? Why?!!

Miserably,
        Carter

Dear God,
    I've noticed that my person buys me more treats when they're colorful and seasonal, like pumpkin-shaped treats at Halloween and turkey-shaped treats at Thanksgiving. I don't care what they're shaped like or if they have colorful icing, but if it inspires my person, it works for me! Please pass this along to treat makers everywhere.

                        Thank You,
                        Cliffie

Dear God,
Dog litter?! Is that humiliating, or what?
I tell ya, the cat is still laughing. Help!

Mortified,
Mitzi

Dear God,
Why are they called "hot dogs"?

Nervously,
Mikey

Dear God,
    Last year I asked Santa for a freezer full of steaks for Christmas, and I got a studded collar. This year I asked Santa for a freezer full of steaks for Christmas, and I got a Harley-Davidson jacket. So now I want to know, is there really a Santa Claus? And if so, could you get him a hearing aid for Christmas?

        Thanks,
            Spike

Dear God,
Don't people have their own toys? Why are they always playing with ours?

Possessively,
Maynard

Dear God,
Why don't people understand that you created the garbage can to be the ultimate dog buffet?

—Big Red

Just Wondering...

Like us, our pets often ponder the
mysteries of life. In this chapter, they ask
God the big (and not-so-big) questions.

Dear God,
     Why don't humans have tails?
Without something to wag or twitch
or hang, it's hard to know what
they're thinking.

                    Curious,
                    Jonesy

Dear God,
    When you made dachshunds, were you short on leg bones? Or were you just economizing?

    —Maggie

Dear God,
   Is praying like purring?

   Affectionately,
   Katie

Dear God,

Is it my fault this cage is so easy to get out of? Every time I get out, my human family gets all worked up and acts like I did something wrong. I myself think it's time to find a talent agent!

—The Great Houdini

Dear God,
        Fur. Fins. Feathers. As a fashion
designer, you are the best!

                    Worshipfully,
                    Coco

Dear God,

Do people have something against birds? "Birdbrain." "For the birds." "Kill two birds with one stone." What have we done to deserve this?!

—Pluto

Dear God,
    The rules in our household are totally unreasonable: "No barking, no biting, no clawing, no fighting, no licking, no drooling, no whining, no fooling." We ask you, What does that leave?! We understand that you once made ten Commandments for people. We hope your rules are more reasonable!

        Can we appeal?
        —Lance, Teddy, Cate, and Kittatinny

Dear God,

My person is very angry. Usually he praises me when I talk, but not this time. Just because I greeted his mother-in-law! How was I supposed to know that The Old Cow isn't her real name? You're the omniscient one, not me!

—Cap'n Jack

Dear God,
Why is it that people can change their coats constantly—often several times a day—while my coat always looks the same? I think a new color or pattern might occasionally be nice.

Yours in black and white,
Beau

Dear God,
      I don't think my people did their homework when they brought home an iguana. Do they realize that it's going to become a six-foot-long monster? I mean, What were they thinking?! Don't you think I should eat it while it's still small and save them from certain destruction?

      Heroically,
      Hector

Dear God,

I'm sorry I ate all the other fish—mostly because now there are no more fish and I'm getting hungry. Do you think my family will get more soon?

—Piranha
Pete

Dearest God,

Doesn't my birthday count? You should see the parties my family throws for everybody else—presents, cakes, and ice cream galore! Don't you think they could remember me once a year?

Left out,
Rudy

Porcia

Dear God,

We Vietnamese potbellied pigs don't get any respect. Our people appreciate that you made us intelligent, affectionate, and endearing, but others apparently view us as barbecue-to-be. What can we do to improve our image?

Respectfully,
Porcia

Dear God,
    Hello again. My sister Layla
says you will get mad at me if I don't
stop asking questions, so I promise that
this will be the last one (for now).
But I was wondering, did you make us
for our people, or our people for us?

                Your friend,
                Linus

Dear God,
     Did you make special colors just for parrots? I've discussed this with the dog, who seems to see only red, green, and brown. Thanks for giving us the whole box of crayons!

Colorfully, Latte

If you (or your pet) have enjoyed this book,
Hallmark would love to hear from you.
E-mail us at booknotes@hallmark.com,
or write to us at

Book Feedback
2501 McGee, Mail Drop 215
Kansas City, MO 64108